# Nuts!

## and

# Is That My Ball?

**'Nuts!' and 'Is That My Ball?'**
An original concept by Jenny Jinks
© Jenny Jinks

Illustrated by Chiara Fiorentino

**Published by MAVERICK ARTS PUBLISHING LTD**

Studio 3A, City Business Centre, 6 Brighton Road,

Horsham, West Sussex, RH13 5BB

© Maverick Arts Publishing Limited May 2019

+44 (0)1403 256941

A CIP catalogue record for this book is available at the British Library.

**ISBN 978-1-84886-440-5**

www.maverickbooks.co.uk

Red

**This book is rated as: Red Band (Guided Reading)**
This story is decodable at Letters and Sounds Phase 2.

# Nuts!
## and
# Is That My Ball?

By **Jenny Jinks**
Illustrated by **Chiara Fiorentino**

# The Letter N

*Trace the lower and upper case letter with a finger. Sound out the letter.*

*Down,*
*up,*
*around,*
*down*

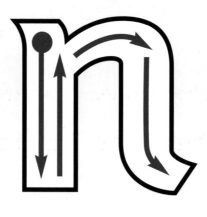

*Down,*
*up,*
*down,*
*up*

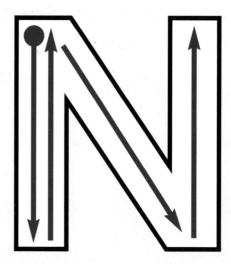

## Some words to familiarise:

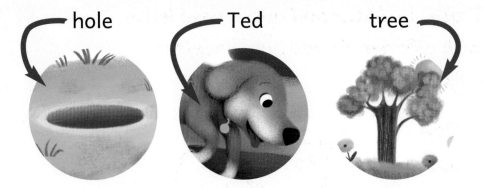

hole    Ted    tree

## High-frequency words:

a  up  the  is  no  he  has  in  my

**Tips for Reading 'Nuts!'**

- Practise the words listed above before reading the story.

- If the reader struggles with any of the other words, ask them to look for sounds they know in the word.  Encourage them to sound out the words and help them read the words if necessary.

- After reading the story, ask the reader what Pip's nut turned into in the end.

**Fun Activity**

Plant your own nut or seed!

# Nuts!

Pip has a nut.

He digs a hole.

He pops in the nut.

Ted digs up the nut.

Oh no! My nut!

Pip digs a big hole.

# Ben digs up the nut.

Pip digs a very big hole.

Meg digs up the nut.

Pip digs a very, very big hole.

Pip has a nap.

A very long nap.

Pip is hungry.

# Pip has no nut.

Pip's nut is a tree.

# The Letter B

Trace the lower and upper case letter with a finger. Sound out the letter.

Down,
up,
around

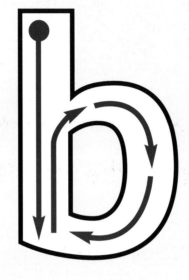

Down,
up,
around,
around

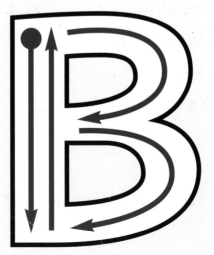

*Some words to familiarise:*

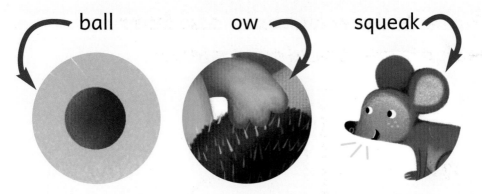

ball    ow    squeak

*High-frequency words:*

no  said  has  the  me  is  you  my

**Tips for Reading 'Is That My Ball?'**

- *Practise the words listed above before reading the story.*

- *If the reader struggles with any of the other words, ask them to look for sounds they know in the word.  Encourage them to sound out the words and help them read the words if necessary.*

- *After reading the story, ask the reader whose ball Tom finds.*

**Fun Activity**

*What else could be mistaken for Tom's ball?*

# Is That My Ball?

Tom is playing catch.

Tom has lost the ball.

"Is that my ball?"

Ow!

That is not Tom's ball.

# "Is that my ball?"

That is not Tom's ball.

# "Is that my ball?"

Squeak!

That is not Tom's ball.

"Is that my ball?"

That is not Tom's ball.

"That is my ball," said Pip.

"You can play with me," said Pip.

Pip and Tom play catch.

# Book Bands for Guided Reading

The Institute of Education book banding system is a scale of colours that reflects the various levels of reading difficulty. The bands are assigned by taking into account the content, the language style, the layout and phonics.

Maverick Early Readers are a bright, attractive range of books covering the pink to white bands. All of these books have been book banded for guided reading to the industry standard and edited by a leading educational consultant.

Pink
Red
Yellow
Blue
Green
Orange
Turquoise
Purple
Gold
White

To view the whole Maverick Readers scheme, visit our website at
www.maverickearlyreaders.com

Or scan the QR code above to view our scheme instantly!